The Adve

Paul
The
Busy Bee

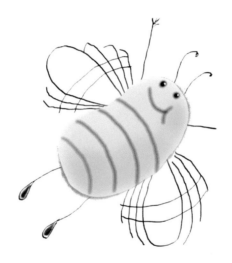

WRITTEN BY SHANI T. NIGHT
ILLUSTRATED BY REGGIE HOWARD

INFINITE GENERATIONS PUBLISHING

ISBN: 978-1-953364-05-0

Infinite Generations
137 National Plaza, STE 300
National Harbor, MD 20745

Special Thanks to my inspiration and the Love of my life—my husband.

A special thanks to my daughter, whose courage and inspiration are my leading light.

To my sons, you inspire me to live out loud.

To my parents, without you, my life would not have been possible. You are the best.

Dear Reader:

Thank you for your purchase.
I hope you enjoy Paul the Busy Bee.

Please share a review of this book on Amazon.

Visit my website for discounts, contests, and/or giveaways.
www.shanitnight.com

Follow Shani Night:
instagram.com/shaninight
www.facebook.com/ShaniTNight

Hi, my name is Shani!

Meet my new friend,
Paul, the busy bee.

Paul, the busy bee is fun to
watch. He's busy all day long.

Hi, I'm Paul.

I'm a busy, busy bee.

Paul, the busy bee with a **buzz! buzz!** here and a **buzz! buzz!** there.

I think Paul is a honeybee.
I've watched him all day.
He's been hard at work in
our garden.

I wonder what he likes
about our garden?

Is it the color, the flowers,
or both?

At night, I'm unable to find Paul. I wonder if he's at home resting? If so, where does he live? I have many questions about my favorite bee.

I think Paul is sleeping now.

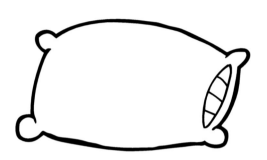

Do you think Paul needs 8 hours of sleep, like me? Oh well, it's time to go to bed. I hope I find Paul tomorrow.

My teacher told us today
that bees search for nectar
or pollen during the day.
And that they spend most
of the day outside,
searching for their food.

At night, they relax and
rest in their nest called a
hive.

My class learned that honeybees need 5 to 8 hours of sleep.

We learned that honeybees are female and are called worker bees.

Paul was definitely hard at work in our garden, but I still don't know what he's going to do with all that food.

-23-

Oh, wait! I have this all wrong.

My favorite bee is a girl, not a boy. I'm sorry, I will name you Paula.

Hi, I'm Paula.

I'm a busy, busy bee.

Paula, the busy bee with a **buzz! buzz!** here and a **buzz! buzz!** there.

Paula has buzzed her face into a flower to search for nectar.

Oh, wait! There's another bee. I will name **him** Paul.

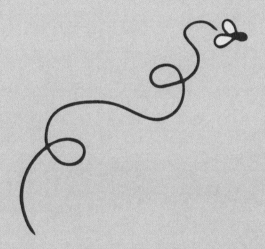

Hi, I'm Paul.

I'm a busy, busy bee.

Paul, the busy bee with a
buzz! buzz! here and a
buzz! buzz! there.

He's definitely a male bee because I learned that drone bees are all male. Also, they have bigger eyes to help them find the Queen Bee.

I also learned that bees don't want to sting you because they die.
Oh, wow! I thought they love to sting you.

Oh, no!

My brother said, "there are all types of bees all around the world except Antarctica."

I wonder if it's too cold in Antarctica.

Wow!

There's so much more to learn about bees. I can't wait.

I wonder what I would do as a bee. How would I look?

I would be a honeybee for sure.

Let's see, what else.

I would enjoy lunch.

I would fly fast,

and I would make honey buns.

I would still have tea with grandma!

I would find nectar to make honey!

The
End

Until Next Time

Other books by this author you can enjoy!

THE TALE OF TWO CARS AND TWO LEGS

THE TALE OF 2'S

SHANI T. NIGHT

The Art Boy Who Won't Share

By Shani Night
Illustrator Reggie Howard

I Am Simply Me

and I love Pie

The Six Horse

WRITTEN BY
Shani Night

Shani and Her Dad

and She loves it!

WRITTEN BY
SHANI T. NIGHT

ILLUSTRATED BY
REGGIE HOWARD

PUBLISHED BY INFINITE GENERATIONS
Grandma's Visit

and Pinocho

WRITTEN BY
SHANI T. NIGHT

ILLUSTRATED BY
REGGIE HOWARD

The Six Horse
My Best Friend

About the Author

What to say?
I write from inspiration and I write to inspire the younger audience. My hope is that we all will continue to let our light shine and not allow it to be dimmed.

Made in the USA
Middletown, DE
13 November 2023

42567026R00027